An Imprint of Sterling Publishing
1166 Avenue of the Americas
New York, NY 10036

ISBN 978-1-4351-6392-8
Manufactured in Zhejiang, China
Lot #:
0 2 4 6 8 10 9 7 5 3 1
06/16

# When I dream of Christmas

Written by Oakley Graham

Illustrated by Patricia Yuste

# Tobogganing

Tobogganing down a hill is fantastic fun
at Christmas time. Although it is fun
to go tobogganing at any time of the year,
it is always best to go when
there is snow.

# Elves

Elves work all year long making toys for good girls and boys. Despite their small size, elves' most favorite thing to do is play basketball with Santa.

# Mistletoe

Mistletoe is a very bad idea if you do not like kissing. Mistletoe is best avoided if your grandpa likes eating onions and has a tickly mustache.

# Snow

Snow is a penguin's favorite thing in the whole world. Penguins only ever make snow angels at Christmas and don't make snowmen as often as they would like.

# Christmas Trees

Christmas trees are happiest when they are dressed in glittering lights and ornaments. Always put a Christmas tree close to a window so they can see their friends outside.

# Reindeer

Reindeer don't receive many Christmas
cards as their names are very difficult
to spell. Despite this, they are not at all
grumpy and help Santa
to pull his sleigh.

Donner

Rudolph

Blitzen

# andles

Candles are a bit like a flashlight but do not require batteries. However, it is not recommended to put a lit candle in your pocket as it may burn a hole in your pants.

# Angels

Angels look a bit like a baby brother
or sister, but they do not wear diapers.
Angels enjoy singing Christmas carols
and meeting up with their friends
at old churches.

# Church Bells

Church bells are the noisiest part of the church. Because of this, they are kept in high towers and nearly everyone who rings them wears gigantic furry earmuffs.

# Holly

Holly is the most prickly part of Christmas and can be used to make wreaths to hang on your front door. Never touch the holly berries as this will make the birds who eat them quite cross.

# Carol Singers

Carol singers have big, red smiley faces and like to sing jolly Christmas songs at the top of their voices. Despite the name, you do not have to be called Carol to be a carol singer.

# Apple Pies

Apple pies are one of Santa's favorite treats. Santa and his elves will never go to a Christmas party unless they are sure it has a good supply of apple pies.

# Stockings

Always hang up a stocking for Santa on
Christmas Eve. Never hang up dirty socks
as this is considered quite
rude and can make your gifts
smell like old cheese.

# ifts

Gifts are a fantastic Christmas invention.
It is recommended that you only
open gifts if they are addressed
to you, as opening other people's can
make them rather sad.

# Snowflakes

Snowflakes are very cold and like to travel in big, gray clouds. When a cloud gets too cold, the snowflakes have to get off and fall to the ground.

# Candy Canes

It is great fun to decorate a Christmas
tree with stripy candy canes.
Never confuse stripy candy canes
with stripy zebras as they do not like
the smell of pine needles.

# A
# Little
# Donkey

Donkeys are very strong and can carry people for long distances. Despite popular opinion, donkeys are very clever and like to play charades, especially at Christmas.

# Christmas Cards

Christmas cards are a great way of sending season's greetings to people who live a long way away. Although they are very thoughtful, most children prefer gifts.

# Christmas Holidays

School can be a fun place where you learn interesting things. Despite this, most children think school is most fun when it is closed during the Christmas holidays.

# Santa

Santa lives at the
North Pole with the elves and is nearly
always laughing or telling jokes.
Santa's favorite color is red, and he is
never ever grumpy.

# Shepherds

Shepherds live on hills and like to race their sheep very late at night. They always warm their smelly socks over an open fire and love eating cookies.

# Wise Men

Wise men are very, very clever,
and always give expensive gifts.
They love to answer difficult questions
but are not allowed to appear on
TV game shows.

# Christmas Lights

Nothing is more fun than Christmas lights in your neighborhood. But be careful not to get distracted and ride your bicycle into a snowman.

# The North Pole

The North Pole is a magical place where Santa and his elves live. Although the North Pole is very cold, they keep warm by eating lots of toasted marshmallows and drinking hot chocolate.

# A Bright Star

If you are lucky enough to see a bright star you can make a special Christmas wish. A bright star is easy to spot because they are very bright and star-shaped.

# Snowmen

Most snowmen have button eyes,
a carrot nose, and like to wear old woolly
scarves. Snowmen do not like sunny days,
naughty children, or rabbits who like
eating carrots.

# Baby Jesus

When I dream of Christmas, I dream
about baby Jesus wrapped up
in a manger, who would grow up
to be our savior.

Merry Christmas!

# When I dream of Christmas…

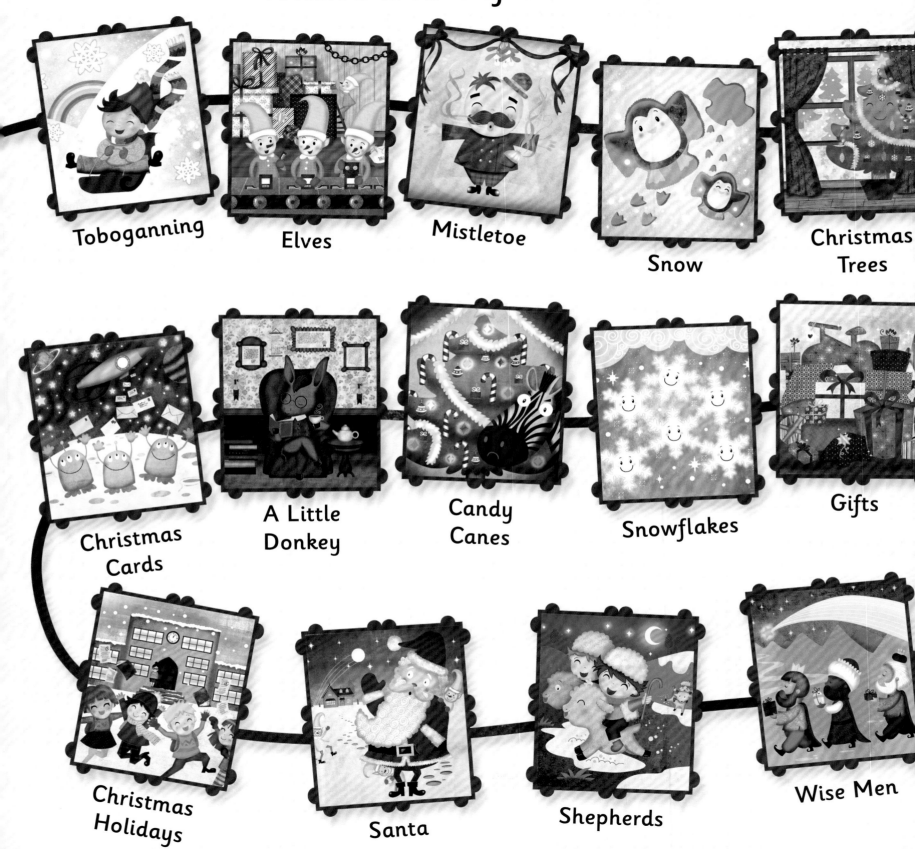

Toboganning

Elves

Mistletoe

Snow

Christmas Trees

Christmas Cards

A Little Donkey

Candy Canes

Snowflakes

Gifts

Christmas Holidays

Santa

Shepherds

Wise Men

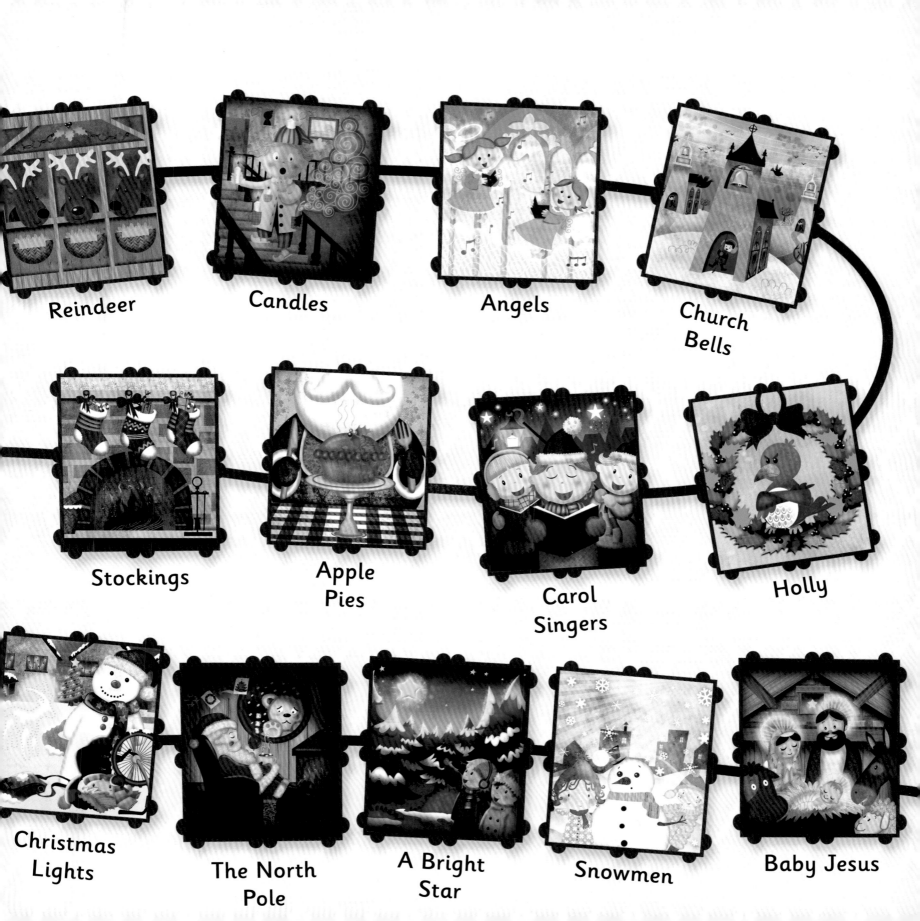

Reindeer

Candles

Angels

Church Bells

Stockings

Apple Pies

Carol Singers

Holly

Christmas Lights

The North Pole

A Bright Star

Snowmen

Baby Jesus